BANAN

Illustrations by Angela Mitson Written by Giles Reed

PUBLISHED BY STUDIO PUBLICATIONS (IPSWICH) LIMITED
32 PRINCES STREET, IPSWICH, SUFFOLK, ENGLAND

The Banana Bunch are three very musical bananas.

Their names are Slippy, Skid and Barney.

Slippy and Barney play the maracas, and Skid plays the bongo drums.

Their home is a Wellington Boot.

Today was Saturday – a very important day for the Banana Bunch.

Today the Banana Bunch were giving a concert for all their Munch Bunch friends.

They were very excited.

After practising their singing for more than an hour, they decided to clean their instruments.

All morning they rubbed and polished, until their instruments were so shiny they could see their faces in them.

Now they were ready for the concert.

Some of the other Munch Bunch were busy too. They were getting the stage ready for the concert.

Button and Spud were sweeping up. Lizzie Leek was mending the curtains.

Sally Strawberry was painting the stage and Tom Tomato was fixing the floor.

But some of the Munch Bunch were not being so helpful. In fact, they were being very naughty.

Scruff Gooseberry was busy hiding flour bags in the ceiling. Billy Blackberry was tipping grease on the floor, and Peanut was making a trap-door.

They were so busy being naughty that they didn't notice Pete Pepper was watching.

The show was nearly ready to begin.

All the Munch Bunch had arrived to see it.

There wasn't one empty seat in the concert hall.

The Banana Bunch arrived too.

Adam Avocado met them at the stage door, and led them to the dressing-room.

"Before you start to sing, you must put on this make-up," said Sally Strawberry.

"Do we have to?" asked Skid.

"Of course you must," answered Pippa Pear. "All big stars wear make-up to go on stage."

At last their big moment had come. Adam Avocado introduced them.

"Attention, all my Munch Bunch friends. This is the moment you've been waiting for: Slippy, Skid and Barney . . . THE BANANA BUNCH."

And Adam Avocado walked off the stage.

The Banana Bunch burst into song.

Then suddenly . . . DISASTER.

The trap-door opened and Skid fell through the hole.

Barney was hit on the head with a bag of flour, and Slippy slipped on the grease.

The Banana Bunch were very angry.

So, too, was Pete Pepper, because one of the flour bags had hit him on the head.

"They did it!" Pete Pepper yelled, pointing at the three culprits. "I saw them doing all those naughty things."

"Then they must be punished,"
said Slippy.

Before the concert could begin
again, the three of them were
made to clean up all the mess
they had made.

It took them a long time.

At last, the show could continue.

The Banana Bunch sang and danced and played their instruments better than they had ever done before.

The Munch Bunch audience screamed with delight.

Everybody had a lovely time.

When the show was over, the Banana Bunch were very tired.

Peanut, Scruff Gooseberry and Billy Blackberry realised how naughty they had been.

They offered to clean all the musical instruments while the Banana Bunch relaxed in their favourite chairs.

The Banana Bunch went to bed
that night very happy.

"Maybe Billy Blackberry, Peanut
and Scruff aren't so naughty
after all," they thought.